Once upon a time there was a hare.

He was always showing off.

'I am the fastest runner in the world,'
said the hare. 'No one can beat me.'

'I bet I can,' said the tortoise. 'Let's
have a race.'

'You are much too slow,' said the hare.

'I will easily win the race.'

'Here I go,' said the hare.
'Here I go,' said the tortoise.

3

The hare ran up the hill.
The tortoise ran up the hill.

The hare ran on and on.

'I can't see the tortoise,'
said the hare.
'I will go to sleep.'

The tortoise went on and on.

'I can see the hare,'
said the tortoise.

The tortoise went on and
on and on.

'Help! I can see the tortoise,'
said the hare.

The hare ran and ran and ran.

'No! No! No!' said the hare.
'Yes! Yes! Yes!' said the tortoise.